THE ROBOT'S GUIDE TO LOVE
a coloring book of romantic advice

drawn and written by
Theo Nicole Lorenz

ISBN 978-0997573817

So you've gained sentience and want to experience the phenomenon known as "love." Where do you find this "love?"

Potential love interests are all around you!

Make sure your love interest is sentient.

Try bringing your love interest freshly maimed flowers.

Grooming is an important part of making a good impression.

Yelling at cute strangers is rude
and will not get you a date.

Do not take the word "crush" literally.

Humans can be touchy about their partners' gender,
Ease their minds by explaining that your gender is robot!

If you were built by an evil organization, you must prove to your love interest that you will not kill all humans.

Do not expect your love interest
to come with an instruction manual.

Use your words, not your laser eyes.

Foreign languages are romantic!
Try speaking to your love interest in binary.

Find out what energy source your love interest likes
before giving them ingestible gifts.

Human emotions can cause alarming leakages.
Remain calm and do not attempt to fix the leak.

Obliterating a love interest's enemies
is not always appreciated. Ask first!

Sometimes you have to face the fact that
you and your love interest just aren't compatible.

If the object of your affection does not
return your love, do not kill all humans.
Killing all humans doesn't solve anything.

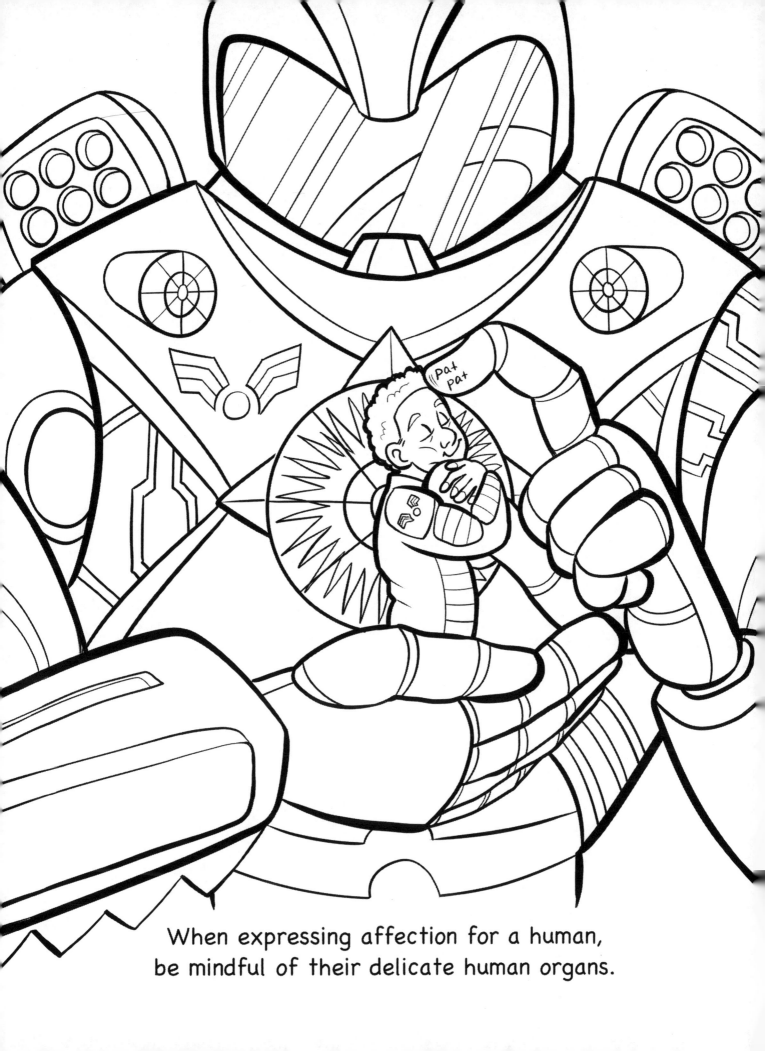

When expressing affection for a human,
be mindful of their delicate human organs.

There are many ways to love someone.
If you don't want to connect to your
love interest's Wi-Fi network, that's okay!

Emotions can be difficult.

Don't try to change yourself to impress someone.
Not even if you can become a rad sports car.

You deserve to be loved just as you are.

About the Artist

Theo is not a robot but pretends to be one a lot, usually to get out of washing the dishes. They live in Minnesota, herding cats by day and writing things like this at night.

Theo is also responsible for *The Apocalypse Coloring & Activity Book, Unicorns Are Jerks: a coloring book exposing the cold, hard, sparkly truth,* and several other unusual coloring books.

This book is dedicated to Pip

Made in the USA
Lexington, KY
25 November 2016